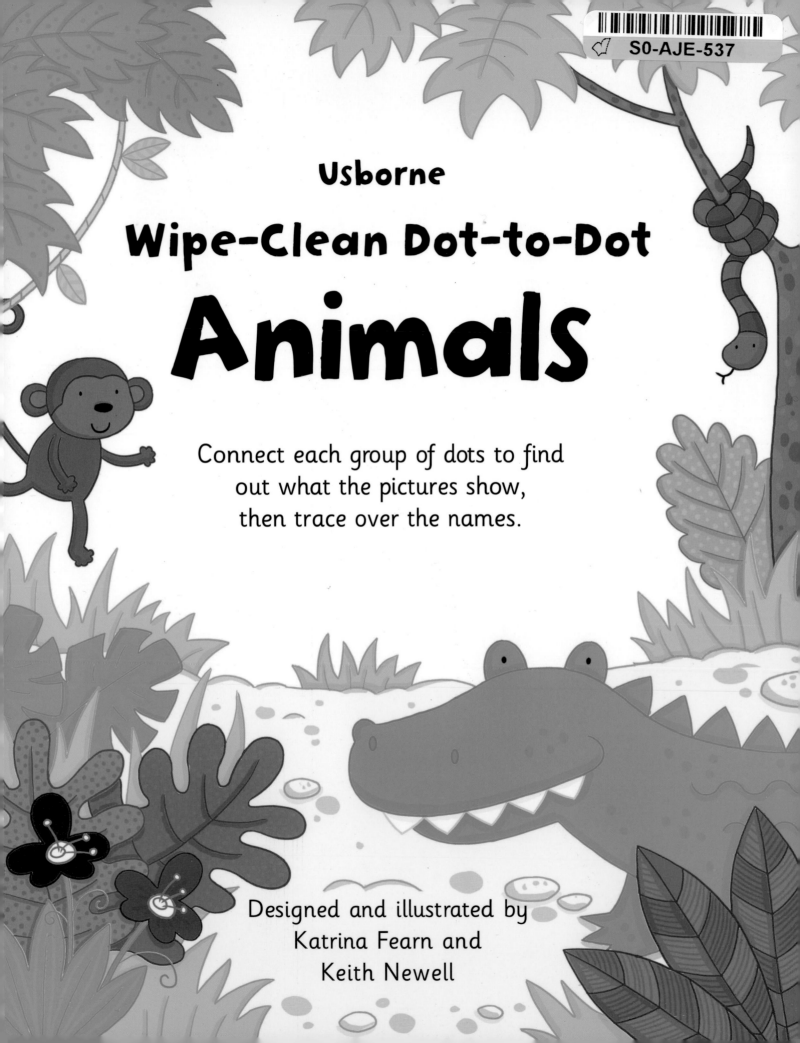

Usborne

Wipe-Clean Dot-to-Dot

Animals

Connect each group of dots to find
out what the pictures show,
then trace over the names.

Designed and illustrated by
Katrina Fearn and
Keith Newell

Who has little white paws?

cat

Who likes to nibble acorns?

squirrel

Who is bathing in the cool water?

hippopotamus

Who has lots of sharp teeth?

crocodile

Who has big ears and a long trunk?

elephant

Who is walking in the woods?

bear

Who likes to jump and play outside?

Who is sitting on a toadstool?

mouse

Who is swimming with the fish in the sea?

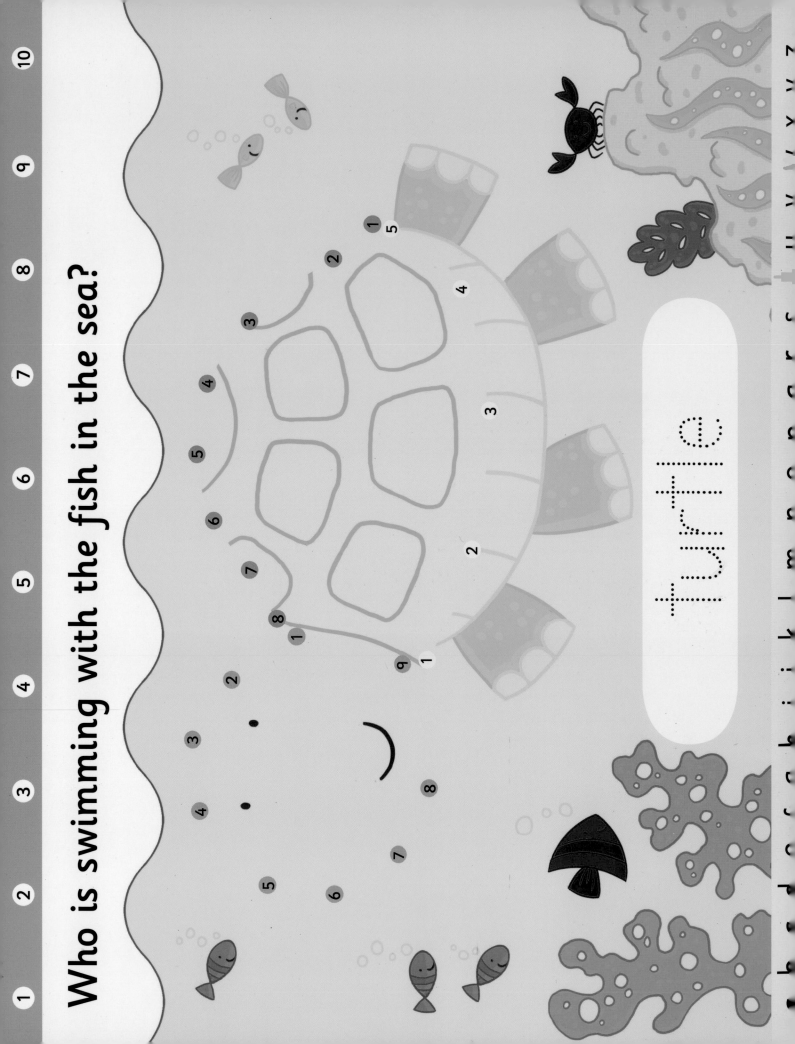

turtle

Who has black and white stripes?

Zebra

a b c d e f g h i j k l m n o p q r s t u v w x y z

Who is swinging through the jungle?

monkey

Who is sleeping in the tree?

koala

Who has long legs and a long neck?

giraffe

Who is hooting in the moonlight?

owl

Who has a big shaggy mane?

lion

Who is hanging from a branch?

snake

Usborne
Wipe-clean Dot-to-Dot
Animals

Connecting dots and tracing over letters
are fun ways for children to
practice counting, writing
and pen control.

Educational
Development
Corporation

Published in the USA by EDC PUBLISHING
5402 S. 122nd E. Avenue, Tulsa, Oklahoma 74146, USA.

NOT FOR SALE OUTSIDE OF THE USA

Made with paper from a sustainable source.
This product conforms to ASTM D 4236.

www.edcpub.com or
www.usbornebooksandmore.com

ISBN 978-0-7945-3484-4

$7.99

JFMAMJ ASOND/18
03548/09

⚠ **WARNING:**
CHOKING HAZARD—Small parts.
Not for children under 3 yrs.

Ink from pen may not be washable.

9 780794 534844 >

1 2 3 4 5 6 7 8 9 10